Teachers' notes

Introduction

The activities in this book aim to support the implementation of the National Curriculum for English, Attainment Targets 4 and 5, Level 1. They are not designed as teaching tools in themselves but rather they offer children the opportunity to practise newly acquired skills.

In order to gain the maximum benefit from these pages, it is essential that they are incorporated into a learning environment which offers time for talking, listening, thinking, reading and writing. There is always the danger with photocopiable sheets that the children will see them simply as time-fillers or 'colouring activities'. Always explain the purpose of the activity to them so that they concentrate on that aspect of the task.

The aims of this book

The aims of this book are:
• to consolidate knowledge of initial letter sounds with the appropriate letter of the alphabet;
• to provide opportunities to practise letter formation;
• to draw attention to sounds within words, in particular to enable the child to begin to separate the initial letter sound from the rest of the word;
• to enable you to keep a record of initial letter sounds with which the child is familiar;
• to develop the child's control of fine motor skills.

The alphabet letters

Children need to be introduced early in their school life to both letter name and initial letter sound for all the letters of the alphabet. Teaching letter names and sounds isolated from the reason why the child needs to know these skills has been shown to have little effect. It is essential that this skill is used at the appropriate time, for example in consolidating sounds a child has requested in free writing.

These pages take each letter of the alphabet in order. The order in which the letters need to be introduced to the children is up to you. It is generally easier for the child to attach a sound to a letter he can identify by name rather than to name a sound.

Suggested procedure

• Select the letter the children need to practise.
• Photocopy the relevant page.
• Say the name of the letter to the children or ask if they know the name of the letter.
• Ask the children to show you how to draw the letter in the air, using the index finger of the

writing hand. Check this for correct letter formation and give help if needed.
• Ask the children to tell you the sound the letter makes.
• Ask the children to point to a picture on the sheet that starts with that sound. Explain that some pictures have been drawn to 'trick' them and that they must choose only the ones that start with the sound of the letter given in the middle of the page.
• Let the children go over the letter in the middle of the page with their fingers. Check again for correct letter formation.
• When the children have achieved this, let them make a 'rainbow' letter by writing the letter outline in four or five colours. Encourage them to try to do this quickly and smoothly.
• Then let the children colour the pictures that start with the letter's sound.
• Ask the children to identify and circle smaller versions of that letter.
• Finally, encourage the children to make a line of letters across the bottom of the page.

Sound check sheets

Pages 26 to 31 comprise five sound check sheets. These offer quick reference for you and the child to see if they can remember the letter sound. The check sheet on page 30 includes letters that some children confuse together. This should only be used when you are certain that the child has a good grasp of all the initial letter sounds. Page 31 is a vowel check sheet.

Initial letter sound record sheet

Page 32 includes pictures for all the letters (except x) ranged around a circular alphabet. You could use this to record letters the child has completed or it could be used as a final check to establish that the child can attach each letter to its initial sound.

Keeping a simple record

A chart similar to the one below could be kept as a simple check sheet for each child in the class.

	Name ....

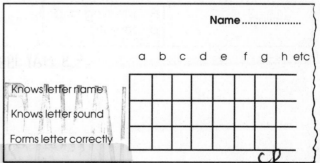

	a	b	c	d	e	f	g	h	etc
Knows letter name									
Knows letter sound									
Forms letter correctly									

Games and activities

Alliterative sentences

Children delight in tongue twisters and they are an excellent way of drawing attention to initial letter sounds. As the children become more confident they may be able to invent their own sentences or even help you compose some.
• Poor Paul poured porridge in his pocket.
• Gorgeous Gussie gave green gherkins to giggling Gertie.
• Lennie the lion loves licking lollipops.
• Winnie the whale whirls in the wonderful waves.
• Horrible Hattie hates holding hands with handsome Horace.

Guess who?

In this game, you say that you are thinking of someone in the class whose name begins, for example, with 'p' and the children have to guess who it is. An extension of this could be to say that you are thinking of someone whose name starts with the same sound as the beginning sound of 'picture' and 'pocket'.

What will you sell me?

Give each child a letter of the alphabet, then ask them to think of something they would like to sell you that starts with the same sound as their letter. The group takes it in turns to sell you things.

Tracking

This exercise is designed to encourage instant letter recognition. Give each child a piece of text (newspapers and magazines make a useful source) and a crayon or highlighter pen. Explain to the children that they are going to 'track' a letter in the text. Give each child a specific letter and ask them to mark it every time they find it in the text. It is better to tell the child the 'name' of the letter rather than the sound.

Further reading

More detailed discussion about teaching initial letter sounds can be found in *Beginning to Read: Thinking and Learning about Print* MJ Adams (MIT Press, 1990). This gives an overview of research into the place and value of phonics in early reading and writing.

National Curriculum: English

These pages support the following requirements of the National Curriculum for English:

AT4 – Pupils should:
• Write some letter shapes in response to speech sounds and letter names. (1a)

AT5 – Pupils should:
• Begin to form letters with some control over the size, shape and orientation of letters or lines of writing. (1a)

NB The programmes of study for writing, spelling and handwriting are also appropriate.

Scottish 5-14 Curriculum: English language

Attainment outcome	Strand	Attainment target	Level
Reading	Reading for information	Pupils, with teacher support, will find an item of information from an informational text.	A
Writing	Handwriting and presentation	Pupils will be able to form letters legibly.	A

● **Name** _____

My 'a' sheet

1. Write in the big 'a' using four different colours.
2. Colour the pictures of objects that start with the sound 'a'.
3. Find four small 'a's and draw a circle round them.

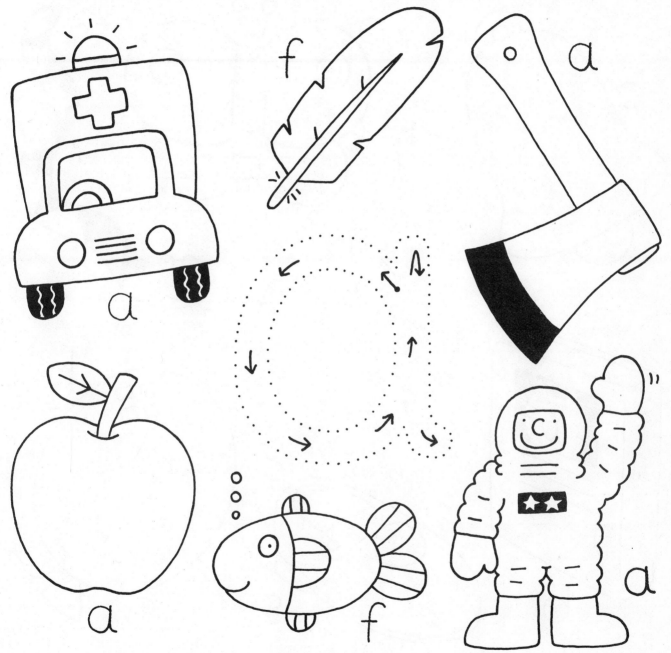

4. Draw over the line of 'a's, following the arrows.

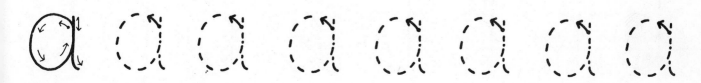

My 'b' sheet

1. Write in the big 'b' using four different colours.
2. Colour the pictures of objects that start with the sound 'b'.
3. Find four small 'b's and draw a circle round them.

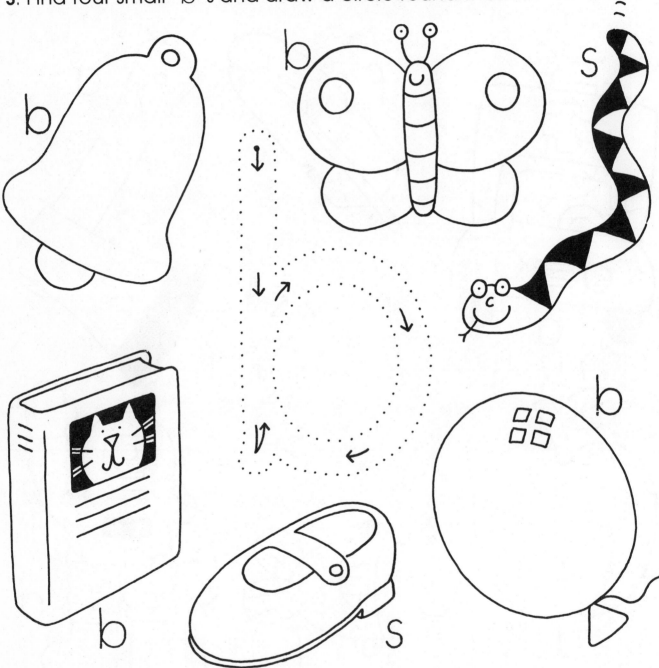

4. Draw over the line of 'b's, following the arrows.

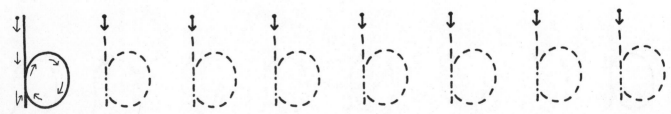

My 'C' sheet

1. Write in the big 'C' using four different colours.
2. Colour the pictures of objects that start with the sound 'C'.
3. Find four small 'c's and draw a circle round them.

4. Draw over the line of 'C's, following the arrows.

My `d´ sheet

1. Write in the big `d´ using four different colours.
2. Colour the pictures of objects that start with the sound `d´.
3. Find four small `d´s and draw a circle round them.

4. Draw over the line of `d´s, following the arrows.

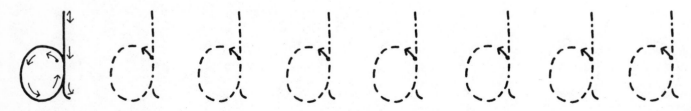

● Name _____

My `e` sheet

1. Write in the big `e` using four different colours.
2. Colour the pictures of objects that start with the sound `e`.
3. Find four small `e`'s and draw a circle round them.

4. Draw over the line of `e`'s, following the arrows.

My 'f' sheet

1. Write in the big 'f' using four different colours.
2. Colour the pictures of objects that start with the sound 'f'.
3. Find four small 'f's and draw a circle round them.

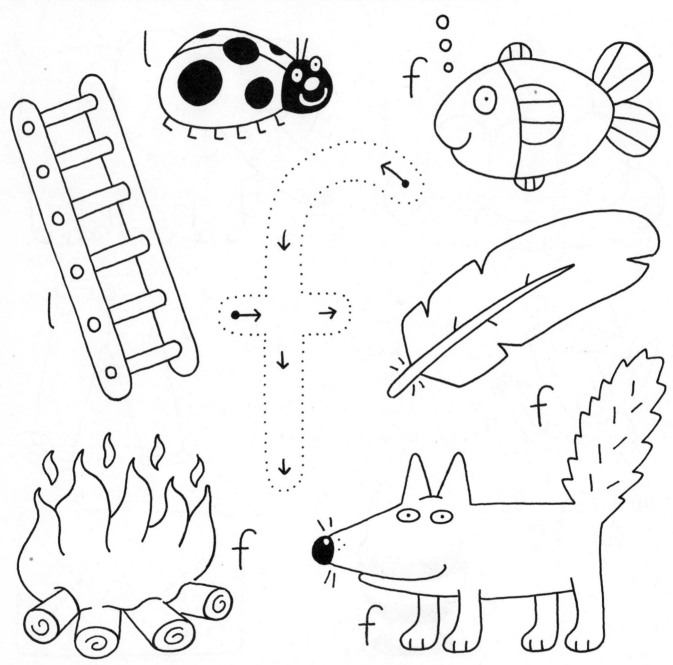

4. Draw over the line of 'f's, following the arrows.

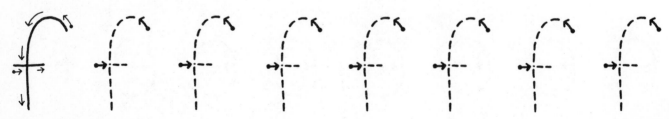

My `g` sheet

1. Write in the big `g` using four different colours.
2. Colour the pictures of objects that start with the sound `g`.
3. Find four small `g`s and draw a circle round them.

4. Draw over the line of `g`s, following the arrows.

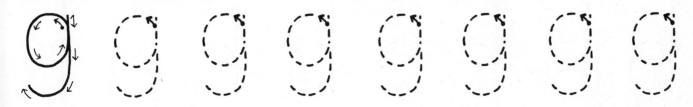

● Name _____

My ‘h’ sheet

1. Write in the big ‘h’ using four different colours.
2. Colour the pictures of objects that start with the sound ‘h’.
3. Find four small ‘h’s and draw a circle round them.

4. Draw over the line of ‘h’s, following the arrows.

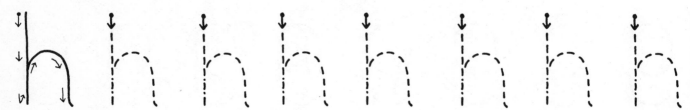

My 'i' sheet

1. Write in the big 'i' using four different colours.
2. Colour the pictures of objects that start with the sound 'i'.
3. Find four small 'i's and draw a circle round them.

4. Draw over the line of 'i's, following the arrows.

My 'j' sheet

1. Write in the big 'j' using four different colours.
2. Colour the pictures of objects that start with the sound 'j'.
3. Find four small 'j's and draw a circle round them.

4. Draw over the line of 'j's, following the arrows.

● **Name** _____

My 'k' sheet

1. Write in the big 'k' using four different colours.
2. Colour the pictures of objects that start with the sound 'k'.
3. Find four small 'k's and draw a circle round them.

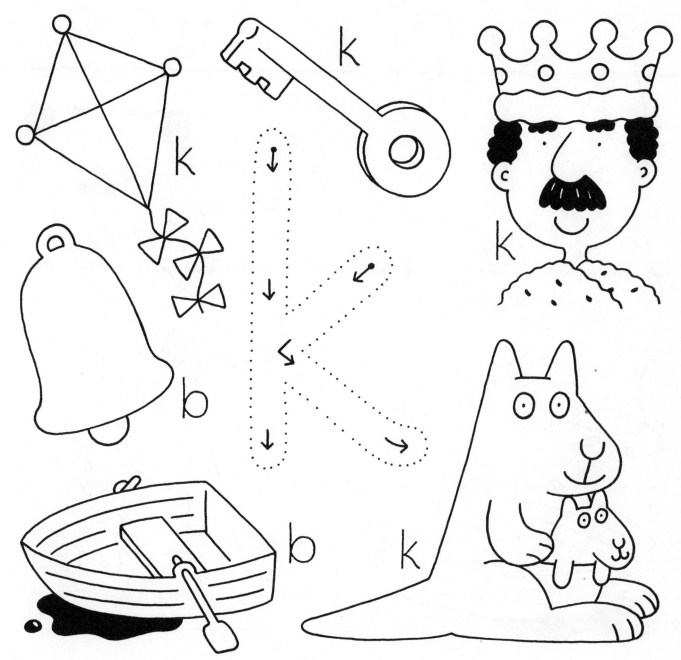

4. Draw over the line of 'k's, following the arrows.

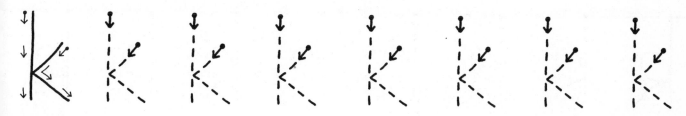

● ESSENTIALS FOR ENGLISH: Initial letter sounds   13

My 'k' sheet

1. Write in the big 'k' using four different colours.
2. Colour the pictures of objects that start with the sound 'k'.
3. Find four small 'k's and draw a circle round them.

4. Draw over the line of 'k's, following the arrows.

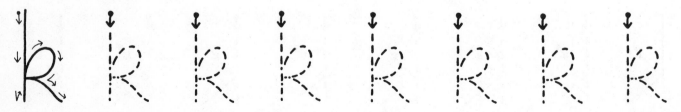

My 'l' sheet

1. Write in the big 'l' using four different colours.
2. Colour the pictures of objects that start with the sound 'l'.
3. Find four small 'l's and draw a circle round them.

4. Draw over the line of 'l's, following the arrows.

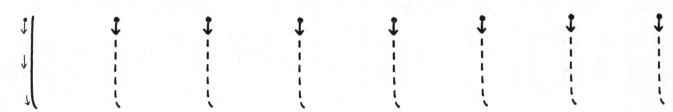

My `m' sheet

1. Write in the big `m' using four different colours.
2. Colour the pictures of objects that start with the sound `m'.
3. Find four small `m's and draw a circle round them.

4. Draw over the line of `m's, following the arrows.

My 'n' sheet

1. Write in the big 'n' using four different colours.
2. Colour the pictures of objects that start with the sound 'n'.
3. Find four small 'n's and draw a circle round them.

4. Draw over the line of 'n's, following the arrows.

My 'O' and 'U' sheet

1. Write in the big 'o' and 'u' using four different colours.
2. Colour the pictures of objects that start with the sounds 'o' and 'u'.
3. Find two small 'o's and 'u's and draw a circle round them.

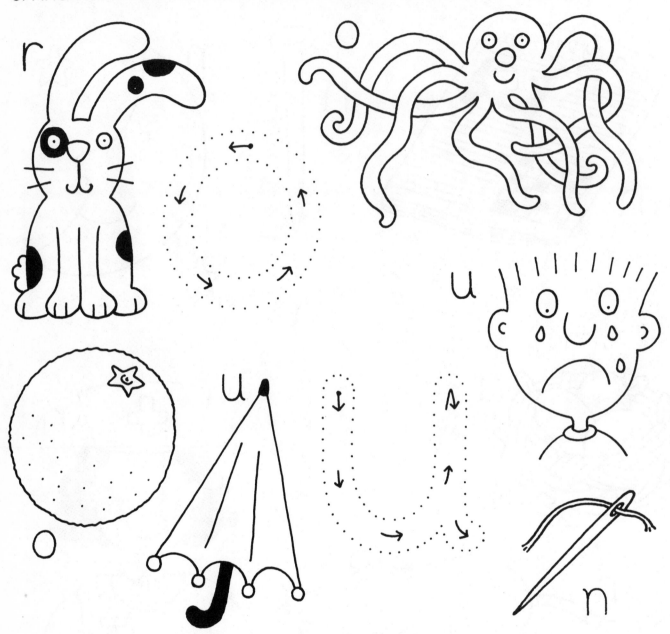

4. Draw over the line of 'o's, and 'u's, following the arrows.

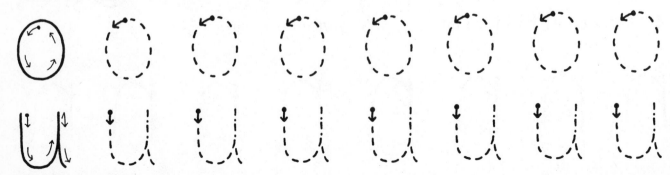

● **Name** _____

My `p` sheet

1. Write in the big `p` using four different colours.
2. Colour the pictures of objects that start with the sound `p`.
3. Find four small `p`'s and draw a circle round them.

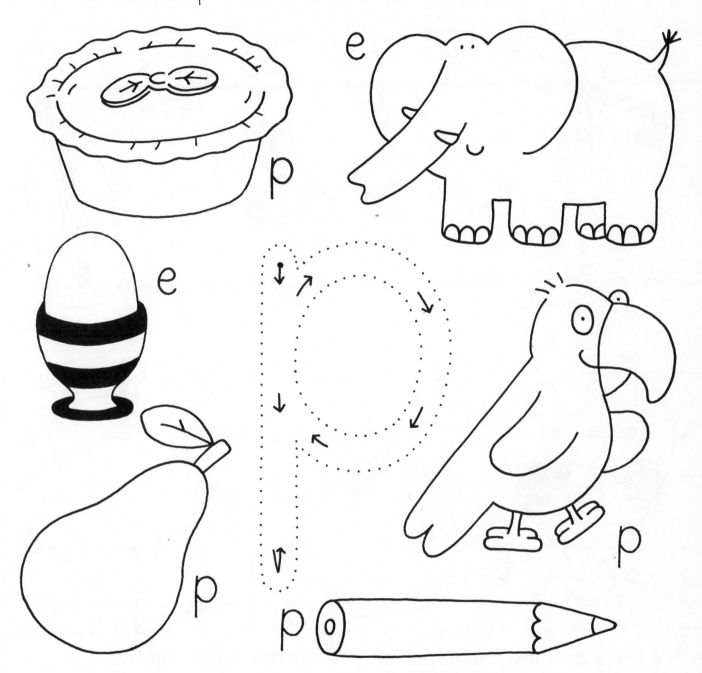

4. Draw over the line of `p`'s, following the arrows.

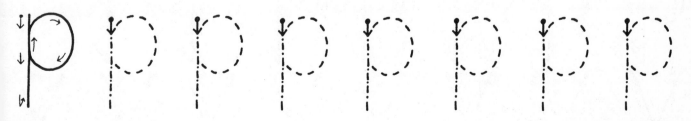

My `q´ and `V´ sheet

1. Write in the big `q´ and `V´ using four different colours.
2. Colour the pictures of objects that start with the sounds `q´ and `V´.
3. Find two small `q´s and `V´s and draw a circle round them.

4. Draw over the line of `q´s, and `V´s, following the arrows.

My 'r' sheet

1. Write in the big 'r' using four different colours.
2. Colour the pictures of objects that start with the sound 'r'.
3. Find four small 'r's and draw a circle round them.

4. Draw over the line of 'r's, following the arrows.

My 'S' sheet

1. Write in the big 's' using four different colours.
2. Colour the pictures of objects that start with the sound 's'.
3. Find four small 's's and draw a circle round them.

4. Draw over the line of 's's, following the arrows.

My 't' sheet

1. Write in the big 't' using four different colours.
2. Colour the pictures of objects that start with the sound 't'.
3. Find four small 't's and draw a circle round them.

4. Draw over the line of 't's, following the arrows.

My 'W' sheet

1. Write in the big 'W' using four different colours.
2. Colour the pictures of objects that start with the sound 'W'.
3. Find four small 'W's and draw a circle round them.

4. Draw over the line of 'W's, following the arrows.

My 'X', 'Y' and 'Z' sheet

1. Write in the big 'X', 'Y' and 'Z' using four different colours.
2. Colour the pictures of objects that start with the sounds 'X', 'Y' and 'Z'.
3. Find two small 'X's, 'Y'S and 'Z's and draw a circle round them.

4. Draw over the line of 'X's, 'Y'S and 'Z's, following the arrows.

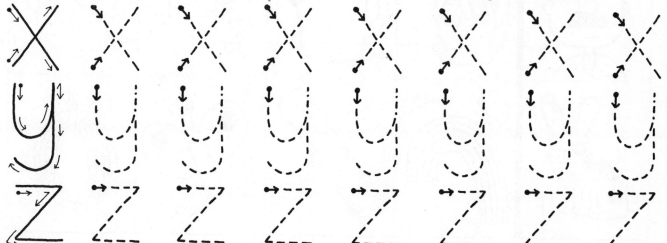

● Name _____

My first sound check sheet

1. Colour the pictures of objects that start with the same sound as the picture in the left-hand column.
2. Write the letter by each picture.

● ESSENTIALS FOR ENGLISH: Initial letter sounds   26

Name _____

My second sound check sheet

1. Colour the pictures of objects that start with the same sound as the picture in the left-hand column.
2. Write the letter by each picture.

My third sound check sheet

1. Colour the pictures of objects that start with the same sound as the picture in the left-hand column.
2. Write the letter by each picture.

● Name _____

My fourth sound check sheet

1. Colour the pictures of objects that start with the same sound as the picture in the left-hand column.
2. Write the letter by each picture.

My fifth sound check sheet

1. Colour the pictures of objects that start with the same sound as the picture in the left-hand column.
2. Write the letter by each picture.

My vowel check sheet

1. Colour the pictures of objects that start with the same sound as the picture in the left-hand column.
2. Write the letter by each picture.

● Name _____

Initial letter sound record sheet

Well
done!